THE LAMB W

Ellen loved staying at her uncle's farm because there were so many nice things to do. She could feed the hens and ride on the old farm-horse, but best of all she could visit the baby lambs. Then one day, one little lamb was orphaned and without its mother's milk it might die; could Ellen help to save it?

The Lamb Without A Mother

Enid Blyton

**Illustrated by Constance Marshall and
Elizabeth Haines**

KNIGHT BOOKS
Hodder and Stoughton

Text copyright © Darrell Waters Ltd 1945
Illustrations copyright © 1974 Brockhampton Press Ltd (The
lamb without a mother, Susan and the birds, The clever weather-
cock by Constance Marshall), 1975 Brockhampton Press Ltd
(The strange bird, The wonderful carpet, The mistle-thrush and
the mistletoe, Woffly the rabbit and Quick-Ears the hare, Jack
Frost is about, The little fir tree by Elizabeth Haines)
First published by Macmillan in 1945 in Enid Blyton's Nature
Readers.
First published in paperback by Knight Books: The lamb without
a mother, Susan and the birds, The clever weather-cock, in The
Fish That Built a Nest in 1974; The Strange Bird, The wonderful
carpet, The mistle-thrush and the mistletoe, The little fir tree, in
The Crab with a Long Tail in 1975; Woffly the rabbit and Quick-
Ears the hare, Jack Frost is about, in The Family in the Cornfield
in 1975.
This edition published 1993 by Knight Books
a division of Hodder Headline PLC
Cover photograph © John Daniels/Andrea London
Enid Blyton's signature mark is a Registered Trade Mark of
Darrell Waters Limited
The right of Enid Blyton to be identified as the Author of the
Work has been asserted by her in accordance with the Copyright,
Designs and Patents Act 1988.
2 4 6 8 10 9 7 5 3 1
ISBN 0 340 60014 4

Printed and bound in Great Britain by
Cox & Wyman Ltd, Reading, Berkshire
Hodder and Stoughton Ltd
A division of Hodder Headline PLC
47 Bedford Square, London WC1B 3DP

*Nine stories
about animals, birds
and plants*

Contents

The lamb without a mother

Ellen was staying at her uncle's farm. She liked being there, because there were so many nice things to do. She could feed the hens. She could take milk in a pail to the new calf. She could ride on Blackie, the old farm-horse.

It was winter-time, so it was not such fun as in the summer-time. But there was one great excitement—and that was the coming of the new lambs!

Ellen loved the baby lambs. The old shepherd lived in his hut on the hillside near the sheep, so that he might look after them when their lambs were born. Ellen often used to go and talk to him.

'Ah, it's a busy time with me,' said the old shepherd. 'Sometimes many lambs are born the same night, missy, and there are many babies to see to. You come and look at these two—a sweet pair they are!'

Ellen peeped into a little fold and saw a big mother-sheep there, with two tiny lambs beside her. Each of them had black noses, and they were butting them against their mother.

'I love them,' said Ellen. 'What do you feed them on?'

'Oh, the mother feeds them,' said the shepherd with a laugh. 'Didn't you know, missy? Ah, yes, the lambs suck their mother's milk, and that's what makes them frisky and strong.'

Ellen watched the tiny lambs drinking their mother's milk. 'Aren't they hungry!'

'Little creatures always are,' said the shepherd. 'They have to grow big, you see, so they want a lot of food to build up their growing bodies. Birds bring grubs to their little ones, caterpillars eat the leaves of plants, young fish find their own food—and lambs drink their mother's milk.'

One day, when Ellen went to see the old shepherd, she found him looking sad. 'One of the mother-sheep has died,' he said. 'And she has left this little lamb behind her.'

'Oh dear—and it has no mother to get milk from!' said Ellen sadly. 'Will it die too?'

'I am going to see if another mother-sheep

will take it,' said the shepherd. 'Maybe she will. She has only one lamb.'

So he gave the tiny lamb to another sheep. But she butted it away angrily.

'Isn't she unkind?' said Ellen, almost in tears. 'She's got one lamb of her own, and surely she wouldn't mind having another. Most of the sheep have two.'

'She isn't really unkind,' said the shepherd. 'She doesn't know the strange smell of this little lamb, so she doesn't like it. Well, well—she won't have it, that's plain!'

'What will you do?' asked Ellen.

'It will have to be fed from a baby's bottle,' said the shepherd. 'I shall put milk into a bottle, put a teat on it, and let the lamb suck.

Ellen stared at him in surprise. 'Can you really feed a lamb out of a baby's bottle?' she said. 'Oh, please may I see you?'

'Of course,' said the shepherd. He took out a glass bottle from his shed. He washed it, and then put some warm milk into it. He fitted a large teat on the end, and went to where he had left the tiny lamb.

He smeared the teat with milk and pushed it

against the lamb's black nose. The tiny creature sniffed at it, and then put out its tongue and licked it.

'It likes the taste!' said Ellen in excitement. 'Oh, lamb, do drink the milk!'

The lamb opened his mouth and took hold of the milky teat. He sucked—for that is a thing that all lambs, all calves, all babies know how to do. He sucked hard.

The milk came through the teat and went into his mouth. The lamb sucked and sucked. He was hungry. The milk was nice. He sucked until he had nearly finished the bottle.

Ellen watched him in delight. 'Please, please do let me hold the bottle whilst he finishes the few last drops,' she begged the shepherd. So he gave her the bottle to hold.

Ellen loved feeding the tiny lamb. She liked feeling him pulling hard at the bottle. He finished every drop of the milk, and licked the teat. Then he gave a sigh of happiness, as if to say, 'That was really nice!'

'He'll do all right,' said the shepherd, taking the empty bottle. 'The pity is—I've no time to bottle-feed lambs just now.'

'Shepherd—let me do it, then!' cried Ellen. 'I know Uncle will let me. Can I go and ask him?'

The shepherd nodded, and Ellen sped off down the hill to where her uncle was working in the fields.

'Uncle! There's a lamb without a mother, so it hasn't any mother's milk to drink! The shepherd says it must be fed from a baby's bottle. Can I feed it for him every day, please, Uncle?'

'If you like,' said her uncle. 'It will need to be fed many times a day, Ellen, so you mustn't forget. You had better let the shepherd bring it down into the farmhouse garden for you. It can live there, and you can easily feed it from a bottle then, without climbing the hill every time.'

Ellen ran to tell the shepherd. 'You needn't carry it down for me ' she said. 'I can carry the little darling thing myself.'

So she carried the little warm creature down to the garden. She shut the gate carefully so that it could not get out. It seemed to like being there, and frisked round happily.

Ellen fed it when it was hungry. Her aunt put

14

milk into the baby's bottle, and Ellen went to
take it to the lamb. He soon knew her and ran
to meet her. How he sucked the milk from the
bottle! He almost pulled it out of Ellen's hand
sometimes!

He grew well. He had a tight, woolly coat to
keep him warm, and a long wriggling tail. He
could jump and spring about cleverly. Ellen
often played with him in the garden, and they
loved one another very much.

He grew quite fat and tubby. Ellen looked at

him one day and said, 'You are almost like a little sheep. Don't grow into a sheep, little lamb. Sheep never play. They just eat grass all day long, and say "baa-baa-baa".'

The lamb could bleat in his little high voice. Sometimes he would bleat for Ellen to bring him a bottle of milk. 'Maa-maaa-maa!' he would say.

But soon there came a time when he did not need to drink milk any more. He could eat grass. He nibbled at it and liked it. Ellen watched him eating it, and was afraid that soon he would have to leave the garden and go into the big field with the others.

'Then you will forget about me, and won't come running to meet me any more,' she said sadly.

One day the big sheep were sheared. The farmyard was full of their bleating, for they did not like their warm, thick woolly coats being cut away from them.

Ellen watched the shearing. 'What a lot of wool!' she said. 'I suppose that will be washed and woven, and made into warm clothes. How useful the sheep are to us.'

16

The lamb was not sheared. He was allowed to keep his coat that year. 'It is not thick enough for shearing,' said the shepherd. 'The lambs keep their coats. They will be very thick next year. And now, missy, I think your lamb must come and live in the field. He is old enough to be with the others, now that you have quite finished feeding him by bottle.'

Ellen was sad. She took the little lamb from the farmhouse garden to the field. She opened the gate and let him through. He stood quite still and stared at all the sheep and lambs there.

Then a small lamb came up to him. 'Come and play "Jump-high, jump-low" with us,' he said. 'It's such fun.'

The little lamb frisked off in delight. 'He has forgotten me already,' said Ellen.

But he hadn't. Whenever the little girl goes by the field, the lamb comes running up to the hedge, bleating. He pushes his nose through and Ellen pats him. And I expect that he will always remember his little friend, and run happily to greet her, don't you?

The clever weather-cock

There was once a cock who lived in a farm-yard with hens and ducks and turkeys. He was a very clever cock, because he could always tell the other birds and animals what the weather was going to be.

'Ducks! You'll be happy tomorrow!' he would say. 'It will rain tonight!'

And sure enough it would rain, and the next day the ducks would go splashing happily through the puddles, and the hens would look miserable.

Then another time he would say, 'Ah, you'll

want to keep in your houses tomorrow, hens! It will be icy-cold! I shouldn't be surprised if we have some snow!'

He would be quite right. Snow would come in the night, and all the birds and animals would look out in surprise at it. Snow! White snow over everything. How strange and queer the farmyard looked.

'Dear Mr. Cock, how can you tell the weather so cleverly?' asked one of the ducks.

'The wind tells me,' said the cock.

'The wind!' said the duck. 'But how can it tell you that, dear Mr. Cock?'

'Well, if the wind comes from the north, I know it will be cold,' said the cock. 'Icy-cold. So cold that we may have snow if it is winter-time.'

'Why is the north wind so cold?' asked the duck in surprise.

'Because it blows over icy-cold lands, I suppose,' said the cock. He was quite right. 'I suppose if a wind is warm, it comes from warmer lands than ours; and if it's cold, it comes from colder lands. You could have thought of that yourself, duck, couldn't you?'

'No, I couldn't, dear Mr. Cock,' said the duck. 'I am not clever like you. Can you tell me this? Why do some winds bring rain?'

'Because they blow over the sea and get wet, I suppose,' said the clever cock. And again he was quite right.

'What a wonderful bird you are!' said the duck. 'It is a pity you have to live in a farmyard like this, dear Mr. Cock, a very great pity.'

'I suppose it is,' said the cock, and he fluffed out his beautiful tail-feathers, and made himself big. 'I know every wind that blows, and I can tell you which one will bring good weather, and which one will bring bad weather.'

'What wind is blowing now?' asked the duck. A big drop of rain fell on his beak as he spoke.

'The wind is warm and wet,' said the cock wisely, 'so it comes from the west, and it comes from the south. It is a little bit of both. It is a south-westerly wind. The south wind is always warm, and the west wind is wet.'

'Certainly you are very clever,' said the duck, and waddled off on her webbed feet to tell the other ducks to come out and splash in the puddles that would soon be everywhere.

The clever weather-cock

Now, on the church tower there was another kind of cock—a weather-cock. It swung round in the wind and pointed to the west, or the east, or the south, or the north, to show everyone which way the wind was blowing.

'If his beak points to N for north, then the wind is blowing from the north,' said the boys and girls. 'And if it points to S for south, the wind is blowing from the south.'

One day there came a tremendous gale. The wind blew from the north-west, and the weather-cock could hardly keep his balance, up there on the church tower. He was old and a bit rusty. He creaked as he went round.

The wind blew harder still—and the old weather-cock was blown right off the spire! He flew through the air, high over the trees, and fell flat into the pond in the farmyard. He lay there at the bottom of the water. All the ducks were very much afraid.

'What is it, what is it?' they quacked to one another. 'Let us go and fetch the clever cock. He will be able to tell us.'

The cock came. 'Cock-a-doodle-doo!' he said in great surprise. 'Why, that is the weather-cock from the church steeple. The wind has blown him away. Good afternoon, weather-cock.'

The weather-cock said 'good afternoon' from the bottom of the pond—but it sounded like 'booble, booble, booble, booble', because the water made him gurgle.

'There's no weather-cock on the church spire!' cried the hens. 'No one will know which way the wind is blowing. The boys and girls will be very upset.'

'*I* will go,' said the clever cock, ruffling his wings. 'I always know which way the wind is blowing. I can always point my beak in the right direction. I will be the weather-cock until the real one is taken from the pond and put back.'

He flew to the top of the church spire, and perched on the bars that said N, S, E, and W for north, south, east and west. The wind was dying down now, but it still came from the north-west. So the cock firmly set his beak towards the north-west, half-way between the N and the W.

'Cock-a-doodle-doo! North-west wind for you!' he crowed to the children.

'I say! Isn't the weather-cock fat today?' said

the boys and girls in surprise. 'And did you hear him crow?'

Next day the wind changed to south, and the boys and girls took off their coats and scarves, for the day was warm.

'Cock-a-doodle-doo! Wind from the south for you!' crowed the cock. He was enjoying himself. He could see so many, many things from such a high place. He could see the whole town. He could see the river curling along like a blue snake in the distance. He could see his own farmyard, and the little pond in the middle of it.

He could see the fields and the sheep in them. He could see the hens and the ducks, looking very small, like toys. Oh, he could see a wonderful lot of things, could the clever old cock!

The winds came to him and talked in his ear. 'We do a lot of good,' said the winds. 'We dry the clothes on the line. We blow the sailing-ships along. We take the big arms of the windmills and twist them round and round to help the farmers.'

'So you do, so you do, cock-a-doodle-doo' said the cock, ruffling his wings. He swung round a little as another wind spoke to him.

'I bring the rain,' it said. 'I fill up the ponds and the rivers. I water the flowers, and help the farmers' crops to grow.'

'Well, don't blow too much just at present, west wind,' said the cock. 'I can't run to shelter myself up here, you know, and I have no umbrella.'

'Ho, ho! a weather-cock with an umbrella would be a funny sight!' said the west wind, and he brought a few drops of rain along and wetted the cock's red comb.

The cock was really very clever indeed. He

always pointed his beak in the right direction, no matter where the wind came from. And he always knew if it was going to be cold or hot, snowy or rainy. He called out the news.

'Here's a sunny day for you, cock-a-doodle-doo!' he would cry, when the south wind blew gently.

'Here's a snowy day for you, cock-a-doodle-doodle-doo!' he would crow, when the north wind blew strongly, and big snow-flakes began to fall from the sky.

The south wind told him how it blew the pollen out of the hazel catkins on to the red-spiked buds along the twigs, so that nuts could be made. The east wind told him how it shook the green flowers of the nettles in the summer, so that pollen might be blown out of them too.

The north-west wind told him how it blew all kinds of seeds away in the autumn, so that they flew off in the air to find new homes.

'I puff and I blow, and off go the dandelion seeds, and the thistle-down clocks, and the ash keys and the seeds from the poppy-heads!' said the wind.

'And you blow the acorns and conkers down

for the children too!' said the weather-cock. For now he *was* the weather-cock. Yes, he really was! No one had found the other old weather-cock in the pond. He was still there, settling deep in the mud.

The new weather-cock was very thin now, but as weather-cocks always *are* thin, that was a very good thing. He always tells what wind is blowing, and he never, never makes a mistake.

Have you ever noticed him blowing this way and that? Look at him and see. You will think he is really very clever.

The Wonderful Carpet

Once upon a time there was a queen who loved beautiful things.

She paid a great deal of money for many lovely things in her palace. She went about looking for lovely chairs, and beautiful curtains, for well-carved chests, and splendid pictures. She hunted for gleaming glasses, and for shining candle-sticks.

At last it seemed as if she could find no more things of beauty. There was nowhere else to look, no other shop to go to.

'Well, I will send out a notice to say that I will pay well for any lovely thing that is brought to me,' said the queen. 'Then maybe I shall get some wonderful treasures.'

So she sent out a notice.

'A large reward in gold will be paid to anyone who brings me something lovely.'

Then there came crowds of men and women, and even children, to her palace.

One man brought a necklace of carved green beads. Each one was carved in the shape of a flower.

But the queen was tired of necklaces. 'I already have one hundred and fifty different necklaces,' she told the man. 'I do not want any more.'

Another man brought a silken cushion, on which had been painted a peacock so life-like that it really seemed to move.

But the queen did not like that either, 'I have too many cushions already,' she said. 'The peacock is nicely done, but I do not want another cushion.'

A woman brought a set of tiny animals, all carved out of black wood. They were perfect, and the queen could see every hair on the backs of the animals.

'I have animals carved in ivory that are as beautiful as these,' she said. 'I want no more.'

A child brought her a bubble-pipe, and she blew her some bubbles. They bounced into the air from her pipe, and the queen saw that they were all the colours of the rainbow.

'See,' said the little girl, 'I have caught a rainbow in my bubbles. Would you not like to buy my pipe, Your Majesty, and then you could catch rainbows for yourself? It is a beautiful thing to do.'

'It is only a game for children,' said the queen.

'I have a bubble-pipe that is made of glass so fine it looks like a bubble itself. I do not want your pipe, little girl.'

Day after day the queen saw beautiful things, and she wanted none of them. She grew tired of looking at them, and she even grew tired of looking at the lovely things that she herself had bought.

'I did not think I would ever get tired of loveliness,' she said. 'Is there something the matter with me, that I can no longer find anything I think is beautiful enough to buy and keep?'

One day a little man came to see the queen. He had a sack on his back, which he put down when he bowed himself very low before her.

'Have you brought me something beautiful?' asked the queen. 'I hope it is not a chair, or beads, or something painted or carved. I am tired of those things.'

'I have brought you something so beautiful that no one has ever tired of it,' said the little man. He opened his sack, and shook out hundreds of little round things all over the floor. The queen stared at them in surprise.

30

'Do you call those beautiful?' she asked. 'I think they are ugly. This is a stupid joke, little man. I will put you in prison!'

'Your Majesty, these things I have brought you hold more beauty than any treasure you have in your great palace,' said the little man.

'More beauty than there is in that wonderful carpet you are standing on?' asked the queen.

The little man looked down at the marvellous carpet. He saw the beautiful pattern, and the glowing colours. He nodded his head.

'I bring you more beauty than there is in a hundred carpets like this,' he said.

'You could not bring me anything more beautiful than this carpet,' said the queen. 'Why, it cost three thousand pounds!'

'I bring you something that will make you a carpet for nothing,' said the little man. 'A carpet more beautiful than anything you have ever dreamed of. Your Majesty, you think that money can buy all the beauty there is. But I tell you that the most lovely things in the world cost nothing. And one of these I bring you.'

'Show me the beauty in it, then,' said the queen, growing cross. 'I can see no beauty in these little brown things on my carpet.'

'Your Majesty, you know the wood that lies to the east of your palace?' said the little man. 'There are trees there, but little grows beneath them. Bury these things I have brought you, bury them in that wood, a few inches below the ground – and I promise you that when May-time comes, you will have a carpet more beautiful than any you have ever seen!'

The queen was puzzled, and a little excited. Perhaps the little man was talking about a Magic Carpet. The queen had never bought anything magic. She hoped the little man's carpet would be enchanted, full of magic.

'I will do as you say,' she said. 'I will bury these little brown things in the ground, and I will wait until May-time – then I will go to see this wonderful carpet you have promised me. But, little man, if I do not think it is wonderful, if I do not find it more beautiful than the carpet you are now standing on, I shall put you into prison for the rest of your life.'

'Your Majesty, if you do not tell me that the beauty I bring you is worth more than all the treasures in your palace, then I will gladly

spend the rest of my life in prison,' said the
little man.

He went away. The queen called her servants,
and gave them the queer little round things.
'Put them back into the sack, and take them to
the bare wood that lies to the east of my palace,'
she said. 'Bury them a few inches below the
ground and leave them.'

The servants did what the queen commanded
them. It was autumn then. The winter came
later, with snow and frost. Then came the
spring, and the queen remembered what the
little man had told her.

'It is April now,' she thought to herself.
'Soon it will be time to go and see this wonderful
carpet that the little man promised me.'

Now, the little brown things that the man had
brought to the queen were bluebell bulbs.
When they were buried in the wood, they sent
out small roots to hold themselves down firmly.
They lay quietly there all the winter.

When the spring-time came, the bulbs sent
up long leaves that looked as if they had been
folded in two, for there was a crease all the way
down the middle. Then the sun shone warmly,

and the spikes of flowers began to push up.

Up and up they grew, and one day hundreds of them began to open out into blue bells – bells that hung down the green stalk, looking as if they might ring at any moment!

The flowers were a most wonderful colour. More and more of them opened until the wood looked as if a carpet of shimmering, gleaming blue had been laid there. They swung gently in the wind, and sent out a delicious scent.

The queen came walking to the wood to see the carpet that the little man had promised her.

She saw the sheets of bluebells in the distance, beautiful to see. She smelt their sweet scent. She saw how the flowers changed their colour as they swung a little in the wind and the sun.

'So this is the carpet!' she said. 'A carpet of bluebells! It looks like a blue lake, a blue, shimmering lake – and it is made of flowers!'

She stood and looked for a long, long time. Then she heard a voice, and she saw the little man standing beside her.

'Well, Your Majesty,' he said, 'do you not think I was right? Is not this carpet more beautiful than the one you have in your palace? It costs nothing – and it is a beauty that everyone can share. It is not put into a palace, and kept for a few to see.'

'Little man, you are right,' said the queen. 'I love beautiful things – but I have always thought that those I paid much gold for must be worth the most – but this carpet of bluebells is the loveliest thing I ever saw. Give me some more beauty like this, little man, and I shall be happier than I have ever been before!'

The little man was pleased. He took the queen to a nearby field, and showed her the golden sheets of buttercups, stretching as far as the eye could see.

He took her to the hills, and showed her the dancing cowslips, nodding their pretty heads in the wind. He took her to the lanes, and showed her where the hawthorn lay like drifting snow across the hedges.

'Lovely, lovely, lovely!' said the queen. 'Anyone can have my palace treasures now! These are more beautiful than anything I can buy. Oh, little man, tell everyone to find these things and be happy!'

Well, we will, won't we? We won't buy treasures and store them away for ourselves – but we will find buttercup-fields and daisy-banks, cowslip-meadows and bluebell-woods – and we will store them away in our minds so that we can always see them there whenever we want to!

Susan and the birds

Susan was very fond of the birds in the garden. She badly wanted to get near to them and watch them. But whenever she crept close, they flew away.

'It's such a pity, Mummy,' she said. 'I only want to watch them, and see how pretty they are, and find out what bird sings so sweetly—but they won't let me. It isn't kind of them to keep flying away. Don't they know I'm their friend?'

'Well, no, they don't, darling,' said her mother. 'You see, most people don't bother about watching the birds, they just frighten them away—so they think you are the same.'

'But I'm not,' said Susan. 'I want to be

friends with them—but they won't be friends with me!'

'Well, you must make them tame,' said her mother. 'Then they will let you come near them.'

'How can I make them tame?' said Susan. 'Tell me, and I will.'

'We will give them a bird-table,' said her mother. 'They will love that. It is winter-time now, and all the birds that eat insects are hungry, because there are so few flies and grubs to be found. They will soon come to your table, and then you can watch them closely.'

So Mother made Susan a bird-table. It was very easy to make. First Mother took a square piece of board. That was for the top of the table. Then she found an old broom-handle, rather long. That was for the leg. She nailed the square bit of board to the broom-handle, and then drove the other end of the handle into the ground.

'There's your table for the birds!' she said to Susan. 'Now, if you spread it with bits of food each day, you will soon make friends with the birds!'

The table was very near Susan's playroom window. She was pleased. 'I can sit in the window and watch the birds hop on to the table easily,' she said. 'Mummy, what shall I put on it? Anything else besides food?'

'Well, the birds would like a few twigs nailed behind the table, I think,' said Mother. 'Then they can perch on those when they fly down. And you should put a bowl of water out too, Susan. They have to drink as well as to eat—and on a nice fine day they may bathe in the water too.'

Susan couldn't help feeling excited. She put a bowl of water on the table, and then she found a few nice twigs in the hedge. With her little hammer and a few nails, she nailed the twigs to the back of the table. Now it was ready!

'What do the birds like to eat?' she asked. 'I know some of them like insects, but I can't give them those. Most of them like soaked bread, don't they, Mummy?'

'Yes. You can give them that—and any crumbs from the tablecloth and bread-bin—and the scrapings from the milk-pudding dish,' said Mother.

So Susan put those out on the bird-table. Then she went into her playroom, hid behind the curtain and watched.

The sparrows saw the food there first. They talked about it quite a lot in the trees near by, and wondered if they dared to go down and try it.

'There is no cat about,' said a brown sparrow. 'Let's go. I'll fly down first and then chirrup to you if it is safe.'

So he flew down to the twigs at the back of the bird-table, and had a look at the food. It looked very good to him! He flew down on to the table and pecked at the bread.

'The first bird on my table!' said Susan in joy. 'What a little dear he is, with his brown coat and dark head!'

'Chirrup, chirrup!' said the sparrow, and at once two or three more flew down to peck at the soaked bread. Soon the table was quite full of the noisy little birds.

Susan pressed her nose close to the window-pane. The birds saw her, and flew away in fright. But another little bird flew down at once and gave a little trill.

'Oh—a robin!' said Susan. 'A lovely red-breast. Look at his red breast, Mummy, and his bright black eyes, and long thin legs. Isn't he lovely? And oh, what a rich little song he has!'

The robin pecked at the bits of milk pudding and the bread. When two or three sparrows flew down again he flew off. 'He doesn't like to mix with the noisy sparrows,' said Mother, who had come to watch too. 'Ah, look—here's a lovely big bird, Susan. What is it?'

'A blackbird, of course!' said Susan. 'Every-one knows him!'

He was a black, glossy fellow, much bigger than the sparrows. He drove them away and began to peck up the bread and the pudding greedily. Whilst he was eating it a bird as big as he was flew down and joined him.

It was brown and had speckles all over its chest. 'What is it?' asked Susan.

'A thrush, of course!' said Mother. 'Look at the freckles on his breast. You can always tell a thrush by those—and both he and the blackbird have lovely songs too. You will hear them in the spring-time.'

'That's four different kinds of birds already,'

41

said Susan. 'Oh, Mummy, my bird-table *is* going to be fun!'

'We'll put something else on the table to-morrow,' said Mother. 'Then one or two other birds will come.'

So the next day Mother gave Susan two bones, one to hang from the table and the other to put *on* the table.

'Why should I hang one on string?' asked Susan.

'For the tits,' said Mother. 'They like to swing on their food—so they can swing on this bone. But the big starlings like to stand on their bone—so you can just lay that one on the table for them.'

It was great fun to watch for the little tits, and the merry starlings. The tits came first. They were pretty little birds, with blue caps on their heads, and blue and yellow coats.

'Blue-tits,' said Mother. 'You may perhaps see the great-tit too. He wears a black cap, and is bigger, so you will know him when he comes. See how those blue-tits stand upside down on their bone and swing to and fro. Aren't they enjoying it!'

Susan and the birds

It was great fun to watch the tits, but it was even more fun to watch the starlings. They were bigger than the tits and sparrows, but not so big as the blackbird. They were greedy, noisy, bad-mannered birds, dressed in feathers that shone blue and green and purple.

'Oh, look how they peck one another, and call each other rude names!' said Susan. 'Oh, Mummy, that one has pushed the other off the table! No—he's back again—and he's pushed the first one off the bone—and now a third one is trying his hardest to drag the bone away!'

The starlings chattered and squawked, pecked and quarrelled. It was really funny to watch them. Some sparrows came down to join in the fun, and the blackbird turned up, but flew away because the table was too crowded.

'I do like my bird-table!' said Susan. 'It's the greatest fun, Mummy. The birds don't seem to mind me peeping at them now, either. They must know that it is I who put the food out for them!'

The birds sipped the water, and once the robin had a bath in it. He splashed the water all over himself. It was sweet to watch him.

Susan and the birds

'Now we will put out something for a few seed-eating birds,' said Mummy. 'I would like you to see the pretty chaffinch, Susan. He will come if we get a few seeds for him.'

So they bought a mixture of bird-seed and put some on the table. The sparrows found the seeds at once and pecked them up greedily.

'Their beaks are very good for breaking up the seeds,' said Susan, watching them. 'They have big strong beaks, haven't they, Mummy?'

'So has the chaffinch, if only he would come and show us his beak!' said Mummy. 'Ah—good—there he is! Now see how pretty he is, Susan, with his bright pink breast, and the white bars on his wings, that flash when he flies!'

'Pink pink!' said the chaffinch, as he flew down to the table for the first time. 'Seeds for me! Pink pink!'

He took some in his strong beak and cracked them well. Susan saw that he had just the same kind of beak as the sparrows, but he was a neater, prettier bird. His little wife flew down to the table too, but she hadn't his beautiful pink breast.

'Mummy, I know heaps of birds now,' said

Susan. 'And I shall get to know lots more, shan't I? Mummy, do you think the birds are pleased with their bird-table?'

'Very pleased,' said Mother. 'And they will pay you back for your kindness in the spring, Susan!'

They did! The thrush sang his song over and over again to her. The blackbird fluted in his wonderful voice. The robin sang in little trills. The chaffinch carolled loudly. It was wonderful to hear them all!

'Thank you!' said Susan. 'You have paid me well for your table!'

Do have a table for the birds too. You will love it just as much as Susan did.

Woffly the rabbit and Quick-Ears the hare

Once there was a young rabbit called Woffly.
He lived in a burrow with his family, and he
was very happy.

'It's fun to be a rabbit!' said Woffly. 'It's fun
to go out in the evening and nibble the nice
juicy grass. It's fun to chase the other rabbits
and fun to play hide-and-seek in the burrows.'

One day Woffly ran down the hillside far away from the others. He had always been told not to do this, but he did so badly want to know what was at the bottom of the hill.

There was a field there. Woffly ran out on to it – and suddenly he met somebody rather like himself. The two animals stared at one another.

'Hallo,' said Woffly at last. 'Are you a rabbit?'

'No, I'm a hare,' said the little creature. 'I'm not very old. My name is Quick-Ears. I hear very, very well, you know.'

'You are very like me,' said Woffly. 'You must be a cousin of mine.'

'I am,' said Quick-Ears. 'And that is why we are rather alike. But you are smaller than I am, and your ears are not so long. Your eyes are smaller than mine too.'

'You have black tips to your ears, and I haven't,' said Woffly. 'Shall we have a race? I am sure I can run faster than you!'

'Of course you can't!' said the little hare. 'Hares can always run faster than rabbits. Now then – one, two, three – go!'

Off they went across the field. But Quick-Ears was right. He was the faster of the two, and he won quite easily.

'Stay with me for a little while,' he said to Woffly. 'I like you. Play with me for a few days.'

'Where is your hole?' asked Woffly. 'I like to be near a hole so that I can pop down if danger comes.'

'Don't be silly!' said Quick-Ears. 'A hole indeed! No hare needs a hole to hide in! He can always get away on his quick legs. His ears and eyes and nose tell him when enemies are near, and he can run faster than any of them!'

'Well, where is your home, then, if you haven't a hole?' said Woffly in wonder.

'I'll show you,' said the hare, and he took Woffly to the middle of the field. He showed him a dent in the dry ground there. 'This is my home,' he said. 'I just settle down in this dent I have made with my body – and there I sleep and rest.'

'I want a rest now,' said Woffly. 'I am tired after our race. Shall we lie down side by side and rest?'

'You can have my place,' said the hare. 'I

will make myself another beside you.'

Woffly settled down into the hare's place, and Quick-Ears made himself another beside him, moving his body about in the earth until he

had made himself a good resting-place his own size and shape.

'I must go to sleep,' said Woffly, closing his eyes. 'That was a long race.'

He slept – and so did Quick-Ears. But after a while the ever-ready ears of the little hare heard a sound, even though he was asleep. His big eyes flicked open, and his nose quivered. His ears heard the slightest sound across the fields. He heard the high squeak of the flying bat, the tiny squeal of a far-away mouse, the brush of the owl's wings as it flew.

The sound came again, and Quick-Ears knew what it was. The red fox!

He leapt up and awoke Woffly. 'Run! Run! There is the red fox coming! Run!'

Poor Woffly. He looked about for a hole to dart into, but there was none. There was only the open field around him. He ran off, right across it, his little white bobtail showing behind him.

Quick-Ears went with him. When they came to the hillside the little hare stopped and listened, his big ears sticking straight up from his head.

'He's coming this way!' he said suddenly. 'I heard the click of his claws against a stone. Up the hillside, quickly, rabbit, or the red fox will catch us!'

'Here's my burrow! Here's my burrow!' panted Woffly. 'Follow me! Follow my white bobbing tail, Quick-Ears. I will take you to safety! No fox can get down my burrow!'

He darted into a hole, his white bobtail showing clearly, a guide to the running hare behind. Both animals lay down at the bottom of the burrow, panting.

'You must stay a day or two with me,' said the rabbit. 'You cannot go out if the red fox is about. He eats hares and rabbits, even big ones.'

'Yes, I will stay with you,' said the hare. 'Perhaps a hole is better to hide in, after all.'

'Don't keep putting your ears up,' said Woffly. 'Put them down flat – like this.'

He showed Quick-Ears how to lay his ears flat – but the little hare kept forgetting.

'I can't hear properly with my ears laid flat,' he grumbled. 'I simply can't hear!'

'You don't need to, when you are safe in a

hole,' said Woffly. 'There is no danger about in our burrows. We are safe here. Do keep your ears down, Quick-Ears.'

The little hare tried his hardest to keep his ears flat, but whenever he heard a noise, his ears flicked themselves upright. Soon they became quite bruised against the roof of the burrow.

'I want to go out of this hole,' said the little hare, the next morning. 'I want to put my ears up for a while. They don't like always being flat. Let's go out and play. We can keep near the burrow, in case the red fox comes along.'

So out they went on to the dewy hillside. The grass was short and sweet. There were many rabbits playing together. It was fun.

'I can see how useful your white bobtails are, when so many of you play together,' said Quick-Ears. 'When a rabbit sees danger, he turns to run to his hole – and his white bobtail flashes up and down, so that all the other rabbits suddenly catch sight of it – and they run too.'

'Yes, it's a good idea,' said Woffly. 'And there's another good idea we have too. When a rabbit smells danger and wants to warn everyone on the hillside, he drums with his hind legs on the ground. We all hear the noise, and we run for our lives!'

The little hare liked playing with the rabbits. He ran races with them, but he always won. Woffly told the others how hard Quick-Ears found it to keep his ears flat when he was under the ground.

That made them laugh. 'Oh, all rabbits hold their ears flat, when they are in their burrows,' said a small rabbit. 'Fancy you not knowing how to do it, hare!'

'I do not know how to do it,' said Quick-Ears, 'but after all, I am not used to burrows as you are. You would not like lying out in the open under the stars, if you came to stay with me. We all have our own ways.'

A curious sound came up the hillside. R-r-r-r-r-r! R-r-r-r-r-r! All the rabbits stopped feeding and looked up, their ears upright.

'That's old Whiskers drumming with his hind legs to say danger is about!' said Woffly. 'I expect it's the red fox again. Quick, we must go!'

All the rabbits were rushing off to their holes,

their white bobtails showing clearly. Quick-Ears did not follow Woffly. Instead he raced off down the hill.

Woffly called after him.

'Quick-Ears! Quick-Ears! Come back! It is not safe down there. Come into my burrow and hide. You will be quite safe there.'

'No, no, Woffly!' cried the little hare. 'I do not feel safe in your narrow, dark burrow! I want the light and the open air! I want the sun above me, and the stars at night. I would rather trust to my quick ears and swift legs, than to your dark burrow!'

'Let him go,' said old Whiskers. 'Hares and rabbits are different, with their own ways and their own likings. Let him go!'

So Woffly ran to his hole, and Quick-Ears ran to his field. Hares will be hares and rabbits will be rabbits!

The two often meet and play a game together – but each thinks his own way of life is best. And so it is, for him!

The Strange Bird

There was once a hedge-sparrow who built a nest in a hawthorn hedge. She laid some sky-blue eggs in it, and she and her mate thought they were lovely.

'Now I must sit on them to warm them,' said the little hedge-sparrow happily. 'You fly off and find me some grubs and flies to eat, because I shall stay here for many days.'

A loud voice came from somewhere near by. 'Cuckoo! Cuckoo!' A big bird with a barred chest perched clumsily on a tree, and looked all round. The hedge-sparrows took no notice. They were used to the call of the cuckoo by now. He sang all day.

Later on in the day the cock hedge-sparrow came back to the nest in great excitement.

'Leave your eggs for a minute! I have found a place where there are many caterpillars, all fat and tasty. Come with me and we will have a feast before the other birds get them.'

The little hen hedge-sparrow left her eggs and flew off for a few minutes with her mate. Surely her eggs would not get cold in such a short time!

When they had gone, and the nest was empty except for the blue eggs, a big cuckoo flew to the hedge. She squatted on the hedge-sparrow's nest, and laid an egg in it. Then she flew off again, for she knew that the two little birds would soon come back.

And now, in the nest, lay an extra egg, not so blue as the others, but much the same size and shape. There it lay, a cuckoo's egg.

The cuckoo never made any nest for her eggs. She was a lazy bird, and did not want the trouble of nest-building or of bringing up young birds. This was a little trick she had, each summer – she put her eggs into other birds' nests.

Soon the little hedge-sparrows came back, well fed with the fat caterpillars. The hen hopped to her nest, took a look at her eggs, and then sat comfortably down on them. She did not seem to notice that there was a strange egg there.

Sunny warm days followed. There were plenty of grubs to find, plenty of flies to catch. The cock-bird fed the hen well, and sometimes sang her a shrill little song.

One day she was excited. 'My eggs are going to hatch,' she said. 'I can feel one of them moving.'

The first egg that hatched was a tiny hedge-sparrow. The egg broke and the baby bird came out.

The next egg that hatched was the cuckoo's egg. Out came a very ugly baby indeed. It was bare and black, and its eyes were tight shut. It seemed stronger than the first baby bird.

No more eggs hatched that day. Both the baby birds were hungry for food, and they opened their beaks wide, and cheeped a little. The cuckoo baby had a loud voice.

'I will help you to feed the two babies,' said the hedge-sparrow to her mate. 'The other eggs are almost ready to hatch. It will not hurt to leave them for a while with the two warm babies.'

So she flew off with her mate. Then the baby cuckoo began to do strange things. He couldn't bear to feel the other eggs near him. He moved about to get away from them, but he couldn't.

He was angry. He wriggled about until one of the eggs fell on to his back. He had a little hollow there, and the egg stayed there. The baby cuckoo shook with rage. He began to climb backwards up the side of the nest.

It was like a steep wall to the bare, blind baby. He went up and up, and at last came to the top. He stopped – and then sent the egg rolling, from his back, over the edge of the nest, through the hawthorn branches and down to the ground.

The baby cuckoo fell down into the nest, tired out. But he soon felt the other egg pressing against him, and once more he became angry. He wanted the whole nest to himself. He could not bear to share it with anyone else.

Once again he managed to get the egg on to his back, and once more he climbed painfully up the side of the nest. The egg rolled from his back – down to the ground it went, and broke. The baby bird inside, almost ready to hatch, rolled out and lay feebly on the ground.

Then there was only the baby hedge-sparrow in the nest with the cuckoo. But the baby cuckoo was now too tired to do anything but lie quite still.

Soon the hen hedge-sparrow came back. She had brought food with her for the babies. She missed the other eggs, and looked round the nest for them.

She fed the baby birds, and hopped out of the nest into the hedge. She caught sight of the broken eggs below, and the feeble little bird that had rolled out of one of them. But she did not seem to know that they were hers.

As she stared at them, her head to one side, a

rat came by. In a trice he had snapped up the baby birds, sniffed round the egg-shells, and then went on his way.

'Our babies in the nest are very hungry,' said the hen to her mate, when he came with some grubs. 'This one makes such a noise. I wish he would be quieter. I am so afraid he will bring enemies to the nest.'

Now, the next day, when the parents had gone food-hunting, the baby cuckoo felt the little hedge-sparrow pushing against him. Again he fell into a rage, and stiffened all over.

'I will throw this thing out of the nest too,' he thought, and somehow he managed to get the baby hedge-sparrow on to his back. It was heavy, but the little cuckoo was getting stronger.

He climbed slowly up the side of the nest. He stood on the rim. He gave himself a shake – and the little hedge-sparrow rolled off his back, down through the hedge, and on to the ground. There the big rat found him a little later, and snapped him up greedily.

Now only the cuckoo was left in the nest. He was glad. He liked having the nest all to himself. He liked having the food all to himself.

The little hedge-sparrows did not seem to notice anything except that they had a wonderful baby.

'He is so big and strong,' they told the robin.

'Better to have four little birds than one enormous one,' said the robin.

'He has such a loud voice,' said the hedge-sparrows proudly. 'And you should see him eat! Do you know, he even eats the hairy caterpillars that no other bird can eat!'

The baby cuckoo grew very fast indeed. He soon filled the nest. He looked funny there, for

his tail and head stuck out far over the edge of the nest.

'The nest soon won't hold him,' said the cock. 'Isn't he a marvellous child? No other bird has such a wonderful baby as we have.'

'I wish you would tell him not to make such a noise,' said the thrush, who had a nest near by. 'He makes such a terrible noise that I am always afraid he will bring the rat here, and I don't want my young ones eaten!'

'You see, he's so hungry,' said the hen hedge-sparrow proudly. 'He has such a big appetite. We can't bring him enough to eat!'

The cuckoo called so loudly that all the other birds began to bring him grubs too, to try and make him quiet. He grew and he grew. He was really enormous.

He had to leave the nest, for it would no longer hold him. He flew into the trees, still calling loudly, in his piercing voice. 'Cheez, cheez, cheez!' he cried.

Soon the little hedge-sparrows had to sit on his shoulder to feed him, for that was the only way in which they could reach his beak. But still he cried loudly.

'Cheez, cheez, cheez!' The robin brought him a fat hairy caterpillar. The thrush brought him two. How they wished the noisy bird would be quiet.

'Isn't he a wonderful child?' cried the two hedge-sparrows. 'Did you ever see such a marvel? He must be the biggest hedge-sparrow that was ever hatched! We are so proud of him.'

'*Hedge-sparrow!*' said the little owl, flying up to look. 'What do you mean – *hedge-sparrow*? That's not a hedge-sparrow. That's a cuckoo!'

'A cuckoo!' said the two hedge-sparrows in dismay, and they looked at their enormous baby. And they saw that he was indeed a cuckoo. What a dreadful shock for them!

'What sillies we are!' they said. 'Oh, what sillies we are!'

Poor little hedge-sparrows. The cuckoo played a very cunning trick on them, didn't she, when she laid her egg in their nest?

The Mistle-Thrush and the Mistletoe

In the woods grew a tall holly tree. Its leaves were so prickly that no animal ever nibbled them. They were glossy and shiny, and the holly tree wore them all the year round.

Near by was a big oak tree. It was green and

thick all the summer, but in the winter its
leaves had gone, and it stood bare and brown.

The holly tree was glad to keep its leaves. It
did not like the look of the bare trees around.
It thought it was a stupid idea to drop leaves in
the autumn.

'Such a waste!' said the holly. 'Why bother
to grow leaves just for a few months? I grow
mine for years.'

'Don't you ever drop them?' asked the oak
tree, bending its strong branches a little in the
wind.

'Oh yes, now and again,' said the holly tree.
'All evergreens drop their leaves now and
again. You will find dry pine needles under the
pine trees, and brown privet leaves under the
privet bushes. And you will find dried-up holly
leaves around my foot, if you care to look! But I
certainly don't throw my leaves away every
winter.'

'You have some beautiful red berries on you,'
said the oak tree. 'My acorns are all gone now.
They have dropped off, as my leaves do. But
you have your berries and your leaves too! You
are very beautiful.'

'The children like to come and pick my sprays of shining leaves and scarlet berries to make their homes pretty at Christmas time,' said the holly. 'I am always proud of that.'

'I have something growing on me that the children come to pick too,' said the oak tree. 'But it does not belong to me. It is a plant that grows on me and takes part of my sap for its food.'

'How strange!' said the holly. 'What is it?'

'It is a plant called mistletoe,' said the oak. Sure enough, growing from a stout branch of the oak, was a big green tuft of leaves, set with dim grey-green berries, like pearls.

Then the mistletoe spoke. 'Yes, I am the mistletoe. I cannot grow as you trees do, with proper roots in the ground. I have to grow on other trees, and get their help to grow my leaves and flowers and berries.'

'I don't like you,' said the oak. 'You are a robber-plant. You steal from me!'

'I know,' said the mistletoe. 'But that is how I am made. I can't help it. I work with my leaves and get some of my own food from the sunlight and air – but as I have no proper

67

roots, I have to get some of my food from you too, oak tree.'

'Each year you grow bigger and bigger,' grumbled the oak tree. 'If you get much bigger, you will rob me of too much sap, and then I shall feel ill and perhaps die.'

'I never grow very big,' said the mistletoe. 'I never grow bigger than a bush. Look – here are some children coming. Maybe they will pick me as well as the holly.'

'Oh look, look!' cried the children, as they came near the holly tree and the oak. 'Holly berries – and oh, mistletoe growing from the oak, as well! We can take some home for Christmas.'

So they cut some beautiful shining green sprays from the holly tree, set with bright red berries. Then they cut some sprays of the mistletoe, also set with berries, but not so bright or so beautiful as those of the holly.

The holly sprays were put round the pictures and looked gay against the walls. 'We do love the holly berries,' said the children.

The mistletoe was hung over the lamp, and over the doorway. 'It is to kiss one another

The mistle-thrush and the mistletoe

under,' said the children. 'It is an old, old custom, isn't it, Mother, to kiss under the mistletoe?'

So, on Christmas morning, they kissed under the mistletoe, and wished each other a happy Christmas. The holly leaves shone in the fire-light, and the mistletoe swung to and fro every time the door was opened.

'It's nice being here, isn't it?' said a holly spray to the mistletoe. 'It's fun when the children shout and laugh. I shall be sorry when Christmas is over and we are thrown away.'

'Thrown away!' said the mistletoe in dismay. 'Oh, we shan't be thrown away, shall we? I shan't like that.'

'Well, I shan't mind much,' said the holly. 'I expect I shall be thrown over the hedge into the field beyond – and some of my berries will lie in the ground and grow into tiny little holly trees. Perhaps the same thing will happen to you.'

'I don't want that to happen,' said the mistle-toe. 'My berries will not grow in the ground. They will only grow if they are on the branches of trees.'

'How queer,' said the holly. 'Well – I'm afraid no one will throw you up into a tree! So your berries will be wasted.'

The holly was thrown over the hedge into the field, and its berries grew into tiny holly trees. But the mistletoe spray was put on the bird-table.

'The mistle-thrushes like the mistletoe berries,' said the children. 'So they shall have them.'

A big mistle-thrush saw the spray of mistletoe and flew down at once. He pecked eagerly at the berries. They were very juicy, and the seeds inside were sticky.

'These berries are nice,' said the mistle-thrush to the chaffinch. 'Leave them for me, please. I can eat them all.'

'You have some of the seeds stuck to your beak,' said the chaffinch. 'You do look funny!'

'Do I?' said the thrush. 'Well, I can wipe them off. Mistletoe berries are always sticky.'

He flew up to the branch of a nearby apple tree. He wiped his beak there carefully. A seed fell off his beak and stuck to the branch.

The thrush flew away. The little seed rolled

71

down the side of the branch sticking to it all the way. It came to the underside of the branch, and stayed there. It was happy because this was where it wanted to be.

'I should not grow in the ground,' said the seed to itself. 'I can only grow on the branch of a tree!'

It put out a funny little thing that pierced right through the bark of the apple branch. It was not a root. It was what is called a sinker, because it sank itself down into the tree.

The sinker reached the sap inside the tree. It fed on it. It took enough food from the apple tree to grow itself a pair of leaves.

When the mistle-thrush sat in the apple tree he noticed the tiny mistletoe plant.

'How did *you* get here?' he sang.

'You planted me!' said the little mistletoe.

'I did not!' said the mistle-thrush. 'I don't plant seeds!'

'But you planted *me*!' said the mistletoe. 'You cleaned your beak on this branch and left behind a seed. And I am that seed, grown into a little plant. I sent down sinkers into the branch, and I shall go on sending more and more, until I have grown into a great tuft of mistletoe!'

'How strange!' said the mistle-thrush. 'And I suppose you too will have flowers and berries in good time – and I shall come along and feast on your berries, wipe the seeds away from my beak – and start yet more mistletoe plants growing!'

'I will make my seed very sticky, so that they will cling to your beak!' said the mistletoe.

'You are very clever,' said the thrush, and flew off on his quick wings.

The children noticed the mistletoe plant growing from their apple tree one day. 'Oh look!' they cried. 'Here's a mistletoe bush growing out of the branch of an apple tree! How queer! Who could have planted it there? *We* didn't!'

'I did, I did, I did!' sang the big mistle-thrush from a nearby tree. 'I planted it there with my beak! Yes, I wiped off the sticky seeds and left them there on the branch. And they grew, they grew. I planted the mistletoe, I did, I did, I did!'

The children heard him in surprise. 'Do you

think he really did?' they said to one another.
'After all, he is called the *mistle*-thrush — so
perhaps he did!'

He certainly did. But you can plant a mistletoe seed too, if you want to! Just press it into a
crack of the bark, and watch to see the mistletoe
grow!

Jack Frost is about!

Jack Frost stood on a bare, windy hillside
one night and slapped himself hard on his chest.
'Ha!' he said, 'how strong I am! See what
I have done, I and the wind together! We have

stripped all the leaves from the trees. There they stand, bare and brown, and dead!'

'Dead?' said the big brown owl, flying softly by his head. 'Did you say dead? Oh no, surely the trees are not dead!'

'Well, look at them,' said Jack Frost. 'Not a leaf to be seen anywhere! See how bare they are. I have killed them all!'

'You haven't killed *those* trees,' said the owl, hooting as he flew round Jack Frost again.

Jack Frost looked to where the owl nodded his big round head. He saw holly trees, standing upright, bearing glossy, prickly leaves and many scarlet berries.

'I can't kill those trees,' he said gloomily. 'I have tried. But their leaves will not fall like the leaves of other trees. I can take away the beech leaves and the birch leaves, I can pull off the poplar leaves and the hazel leaves, for the wind to blow into ditches – but I cannot take away the leaves of the holly or the yew, the pines or the firs! They are tough leaves. The trees will not let them go.'

'And a good thing too!' hooted the owl. 'I am sorry to hear you have killed the other trees.

I hope you are wrong, Jack Frost. I *think* you are wrong!'

The owl flew away. Jack Frost went down the hill, and his icy breath froze everything before him. His cold fingers nipped the noses and feet of any animal he met. The birds hidden in the ivy, and in the evergreen trees, shivered when he passed by, tucking their little heads under their wings as closely as they could.

All that winter Jack Frost walked out, strong and cold and fierce. The trees stood bare and brown. 'I certainly have killed them all,' said Jack Frost. 'Soon the woodmen will say, "They are dead. We will chop them down."'

But the woodmen didn't say that. Instead, the brown owl came to find Jack Frost, and hooted with laughter at him.

'You were wrong after all, Jack Frost. You have not killed a single tree! They are all alive!'

'How do you know that?' asked Jack Frost. 'They have not shown a single leaf, not a tiny flower!'

'Put your ear to the trunks of the trees,' said the owl. 'Listen well. You will hear the sap rising in the trees, life welling up in every one of them! They are not dead.'

Jack Frost put his ear to the trunk of a chestnut tree and listened. His sharp ear heard the sound of sap slowly rising in the tree – rising to every twig, every bud – life that would swell out the buds and bring strength to the tiny leaves folded there.

Jack Frost frowned. So the trees were not dead. There was life inside them. He looked at the chestnut tree, and saw its buds. Already it seemed as if they were bigger.

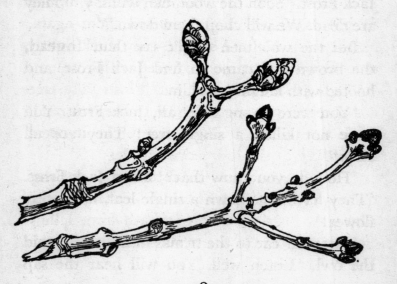

'There are leaves inside the buds,' said Jack Frost to himself. 'I must kill the buds, so that the leaves will not unfold. No tree can live without leaves. I will pinch the buds with my cold fingers and kill them.'

He breathed his cold breath over the big chestnut tree. He felt the buds gently with his icy fingers that could kill whatever they touched.

And then he went away. But the next night when he came back, the chestnut buds were just a little bigger! Jack Frost was astonished.

'Now why did they not die when I nipped them?' he thought. He touched them again, roughly – and lo and behold, they stuck tightly to his fingers. They were covered with glue!

'They are sticky!' said Jack Frost. 'The tree has covered its buds with gum to keep me out!'

He tore a bud from a twig, broke it open, and looked at the tiny leaves inside.

'They are wrapped in cotton-wool to keep them warm! The brown bud-scales are covered with gum to stop my icy breath from killing the leaves beneath. I can do nothing with this tree!'

He was right. The chestnut buds were too well protected for Jack Frost to harm them. They grew and swelled, full of life.

Jack Frost went to the ash tree, and looked at the black buds there. He felt them. They were hard and tough. He could not kill the little leaves inside.

He went to other trees and felt along the twigs for the buds. Life was swelling in each one of them. But how well the trees had looked after their buds!

Some baby leaves were wrapped in cotton-wool, as were the chestnut's. Some had furry down on them, and others had silky hairs that kept them warm. Some had lined the insides of the bud-scales with gum, so that Jack Frost could not possibly get through.

The owl saw him fingering the buds of the trees, and hooted with laughter again. 'Are you trying to kill the trees once more?' he asked. 'Are you stronger than life itself? You cannot stop the buds from leafing, you cannot stop the flowers from blossoming, nor the plants from fruiting!'

'Sometimes I can,' said Jack Frost.

'Now and again, now and again,' said the owl. 'But that is all. The trees will beat you nearly every time, Jack Frost. They will look after their precious buds, so that when the warm spring-time comes, and you are gone, every tree will be covered with thousands of tender green leaves, waving in the sun.'

Jack Frost was very angry. He came to another tree, and looked at it in astonishment. It was a plane tree.

'What's the matter?' said the owl. 'You look surprised.'

'I am!' said Jack Frost. 'Do you see this tree? Well, I knew that its buds were very tender, and could easily be killed by my cold fingers. I came to pinch them just before the leaves fell – and although I looked up the tree and down, there was not a bud to be seen, not one – only the big leaves, changing their colour because it was autumn.'

'Did you say it had no buds?' said the owl, also looking at the plane tree. 'Why, it is covered in buds from top to toe!'

'I know,' said Jack Frost. 'That is what puzzles me. Where were these buds when I last came? I could not find them anywhere.'

'Aha! Don't you know?' said the owl. 'Well, I will tell you, for I know the secret!'

The owl told Jack Frost, and now I will tell you! It is a strange little secret, and you must see it for yourself when you can.

'The plane tree knows that you will come to look for its buds and nip them,' said the owl. 'So it plays a trick on you, Jack Frost! It hides them all – but they are on the tree just the same! When you came to look for them in the autumn, when the big plane leaves were changing colour, those buds were there – and you couldn't see them!'

'Where were they?' said Jack Frost. 'I don't believe you, brown owl!'

'I'll tell you where they were,' said the owl. 'It won't matter my telling you, because you will never be able to get at the buds in the autumn-time, when they are weak and tender. Now they are strong, and you cannot hurt them.'

'Tell me quickly where they were!' said Jack Frost impatiently. So the owl told him.

'Do you remember the big plane leaves?'

he said. 'They each had long stalks, that were very fat at the bottom. Well, Jack Frost, they were fat because each stalk fitted very nearly over – a bud!'

'Well, well, well!' said Jack Frost. 'So that's why I couldn't find any plane buds last autumn. They were all hiding at the bottom of the leaf-stalks. A very clever idea. Too clever for me. I shall go away. I am tired of looking for buds to pinch!'

So he went away, and all the trees were glad. They are opening their buds now, unafraid. Go and look at them.

The Little Fir-Tree

Once upon a time there was a little fir-tree, not much bigger than you. It grew in a forest on the mountainside. It was an evergreen, so it did not drop all its narrow green leaves in the autumn, but held on to some of them all the year round.

Many little fir-trees grew around it. Near by were some full-grown firs, tall and straight and strong. Sometimes men came to cut them down and send them away.

Then the little fir-tree would wonder where they were going, and would feel sad.

'It is dreadful to be cut down,' said the little tree. 'Dreadful to have our branches sawn off, and to be nothing but a straight pole!'

'Do not be sad,' said a big fir-tree near by. 'We are going to be made into straight telegraph poles – and some of us will be the masts of ships. Ah, that's a grand end for a fir-tree – to be

planted in a ship, and to hold the flapping sails
that send the ship along!'

The little fir-tree thought that would indeed
be a grand life. It hoped that when it had grown
tall and straight, it too would end as a mast in a
ship.

'It would be grand to drive along over the
water, hearing the wind once again, being of

use for many, many years,' thought the little fir-tree.

All the small, growing fir-trees hoped the same thing, and they grew a little each year. Then one winter there came a great storm.

It broke on the mountain-side where the forest of fir-trees grew. It sent a great wind blowing through their branches.

'We shall fall, we shall fall!' said the fir-trees, and their branches tossed and shouted in the wind.

'We have no deep roots!' they said. 'Do not blow so hard, wind! You will blow us over!'

'You should grow big deep roots,' said the wind. 'I cannot up-root the strong oak, because it sends its roots deep down. But your roots are too near the surface!'

One big fir-tree gave a deep groan. The wind had blown so strongly against it that it was pulled right out of the ground. It toppled over – it fell!

It crashed against the next fir-tree and made that fall too. That one fell against a third tree, and down this went as well. Crash! Crash! Crash!

Each falling tree hit the one next to it, and soon many were falling like a row of dominoes, through the forest. The last one fell on the little fir-tree, and pulled it up by its roots.

The gale died down. The sun came out. Men came into the forest to see what trees had been blown down.

'Look – a great path has been made in the forest, by one tree uprooting the next,' said one of the men. 'We will clear away the fallen trees.'

So, very soon, the sound of axes was heard in the forest, and one after another of the fallen trees was chopped away from its roots, its branches trimmed off, and it was taken away to be made into a telegraph pole, or the mast of a ship.

The men came to the little fir-tree, which had been up-rooted by the last falling tree. 'Look,' said one, 'here is a young tree uprooted. It is almost dead.'

'Give it a chance,' said another man. 'We will replant it and see if it will grow.'

So they put the little fir-tree back into the ground and stamped down the earth around its roots.

The little tree was almost dead. Its roots were half-frozen. It felt ill and weak.

But soon its roots took firm hold of the earth again, and began to feed the tree. It felt better. Its branches stiffened a little. It put its topmost spoke straight. All spruce firs have a spear at the top, which they stick straight upwards to the sky. The little fir-tree was glad to point its spike up again too.

But, because it had been up-rooted for so long, the little fir-tree did not grow well. It was short and stunted. It did not grow freely upwards as the other young trees did. It remained small and short, not much bigger than you.

'You must try to grow,' said the other trees. 'If you don't, you will be pulled up and burnt, for you will be of no use to anyone. Try to grow, little fir-tree.'

'I am trying,' said the little tree. 'But something has happened to me. I am afraid I shall always be small. I have lost the power of growing.'

It did grow a very little – but by the time the other firs were tall and straight, the little fir-tree was very tiny still. It was sad.

'I know I shall be thrown away,' it said to itself. 'I know I shall. I did want to be of some use in the world – but now I shan't be. When the men come to look at the other young trees they will think they are fine – but they are sure to pull me up.'

Sure enough, when the men came round just before Christmas, they were very pleased with the other young firs – but they did not think much of the little one.

'This is a poor tree,' said one. 'It will never be any good.'

They went on, into the forest. But later on one of the men came back to the little fir-tree. He dug round its roots, and then pulled it out of the ground. He put it over his shoulder.

'Goodbye!' called the little fir-tree to all its friends. 'Goodbye! I am going to be thrown away. I am of no use. But I wanted to be, I did want to be!'

The man walked down the mountain-side with the little tree. He came to a cosy house, with lights shining from the windows, for it was almost dark. He stamped into the house, shook the snow off his shoulders, and called loudly:

'Peter! Ann! I've got something for you!' Two children came running out, and they shouted for joy to see the dear little fir-tree.

'Oh, what a dear little tree! It's just the right size!'

Then a good many things happened that puzzled the little fir-tree very much. It was put into a big tub. The tub was wound round and round with bright red silk, and looked very gay.

Then clips were put on the branches of the little tree, and candles were stuck into the clips! Soon it had candles from top to bottom!

Then bright, shining ornaments were hung from every branch. Some were blue, some were red, some were green and some were yellow. They were very lovely, made of the finest glass.

'I am beautiful!' said the little tree in surprise. 'I may be small and under-grown – but how lovely I am, dressed in these shining things! How the children must love me!'

Then other things were hung on the little tree – presents wrapped in bright paper. Some of them pulled down the branches, for they were heavy, but the little tree didn't mind. It was too happy to mind anything.

The Little fir tree

Strings of glittering tinsel were hung everywhere on the tree. And then, at the very top, a wonderful fairy doll was put, with a silver crown and wand, and a fluffy frock that stood out all round her.

'I never saw such a beautiful tree as you!' said the fairy doll. 'Never! I am proud to be at the top of you. You have a nice straight spike there that I can lean against.'

'All spruce firs have those spikes at the top,' said the fir-tree proudly. 'That is how you can tell us from other fir-trees. Why have the children made me so beautiful, little doll?'

'You are their Christmas tree!' said the doll. 'Didn't you know that children take little fir-trees at Christmas time, dress them up, and hang their presents there? Ah, it is a wonderful thing to be a Christmas tree, and bring happiness and joy to many people.'

'I am glad I didn't grow,' said the little tree. 'Oh, I *am* glad I didn't grow. Once I wanted to be the mast of a ship. Now I am glad to be a Christmas tree.'

It shone softly when the candles were lighted. 'We have never had such a lovely Christmas tree before,' said Peter. 'Isn't it beautiful? Its branches are just the right size. It is a dear little tree.'

'We will plant it out in the garden when Christmas is over,' said their mother. 'Then it will take root there – and maybe next year, we can dig it up again and have it once more for our tree!'

'And the year after – and the year after!' cried the children.

So I expect they will. What a lovely life for the little fir-tree – to grow in the wind and the sun all the year – and to be a shining Christmas tree in the winter!